a gift for

from

Editorial Director: Todd Hafer
Editor: Jeff Morgan
Art Director: Kevin Swanson
Designer: Michelle Nicolier
Production Art: Dan Horton

Printed and bound in China.

ISBN: 1-59530-135-6

First Edition, September 2006

10 9 8 7 6 5 4 3 2 1

BOK2066

**dogs**

antics & attitudes

GIFT BOOKS
from Hallmark

Here's the deal: Play ball with me, or I'll look pathetic and make you feel bad all day.

Aaargh!
And what might ye
be starin' at, ye scurvy dog?

Thank goodness!
At least HE leaves the lid up
on the automatic water dish.

Oooh! I like this feature.

My work here is done.

Don't get too comfortable down there, Fluffy. I had beans for dinner.

Yeah, this costume's a real funny trick. I left you a treat on the sofa.

I'm gonna have to make it on personality.

Oh, yeah. Chicks dig me.

Sugar lapped up the bottle of tequila she broke to hide the evidence.

And next, I splash on
a little Eau du Tail.

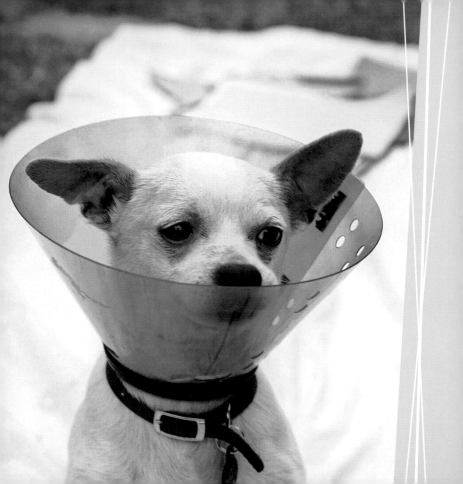

I'm really hoping
it doesn't rain.

OK, shorty, now you pull
and I'LL ride for a while.

Elmo had always dreamed of being a swinger.

How 'bout I get breakfast
and THEN you get beautiful?

Actually, I look better in turquoise.

It's hard to be a
lap dog when the
laps are gone all day.

Here's something else
you can get "fixed"!

The last refuge of the
pork chop thief.

Uh, mind if I chew your
ear for a while?

It ain't exactly toilet water,
but it's not bad.

This super-sizing thing
is way out of hand.

Surely they're not
referring to MOI!

I'm a dog who digs the beach.

It's amazing what you'll wear after a few tequilas.

Houston, we have a problem.

Hey there, sweet thing!

Who needs water rescue
and a leg hump?

Mmm...a full-bodied, woodsy flavor with a lovely, delicate aroma.

...and that cloud over there looks just like a rabbit.

Uh, about that down-filled pillow,
it's not exactly FILLED anymore.

Fork?
I don't need no stinkin' fork.

Whew! Boy! TV has really gone to the humans.

Car keys? Did you say car keys?
Oh, good! Oh, yeah!

Aim high!

Look! Look! I'm an AIRdale.

It's not wise to disturb the queen of the house when she's napping.

Oh, the places I'll lick!

I'm too sexy for my hat.

Every dog has his day...
and this one's mine.

Now THAT was a party!

Oh, those poor dogs! They
have to WALK around the block.

You may think this is gross, but the kid's like a brother to me. So I let him share.

There will be more tree to pee
on if it's lying on its side.

There must be a bird in
here somewhere.